Tales
to
Tell

Going Home - A book about facing death.

Listen - A book about prayer and praying.

Tales to Tell

For School Assemblies - Churches Etc.

by

REV. CLIFFORD W. CHESWORTH

Date of Publication :
June 1998
2nd Edition September 1998

Published by:
Bourne Publications
P.O. Box 61
Carlisle
CA8 1SP

Printed by :
ProPrint
Riverside Cottage
Great North Road
Stibbington
Peterborough
PE8 6LR

ISBN: 0 9528568 2 4

CONTENTS

Page No

FOREWORD

In my work as Headteacher of a school for pupils with severe and profound learning and physical difficulties I have sadly attended a number of funerals; pupils, with only a limited life expectancy, who have died with rare syndromes and parents who die tragically leaving a young family.

I recently attended a funeral for a young mother of one of our pupils who died tragically and suddenly leaving five young children. The service was held at the Chapel of Rest at our local crematorium, which is not an inviting place. The funeral service was conducted by Rev. Chesworth who was not known to me at that time and I did wonder how he would relate to the family and our pupils.

During the service, Rev. Chesworth directed his entire attention to the children and the remainder of the congregation were simply onlookers but very privileged ones.

The children were told a story about a butterfly, which had a very short life compared to a lady, aged 94, whose funeral he had conducted the previous day. He explained how time was not the important issue, although at the moment it might seem that way as the pupil's mother was very young. Rev. Chesworth hoped the children would come to see that the beauty and richness, as in the butterfly's life, was really more important than the length of a life. He pointed out that their mother had helped prepare them for their life which could be an adventure and a wonderful experience.

The telling of the story had the effect of imparting a sense of peace, calm and purpose to the whole congregation.

Listening to such a good kind man who had spent his life serving others in the Ministry I was interested to learn he had been a Chaplain for four years during the war. He was under fire on the beaches at Normandy and saw the fires of Belsen raging. The Rev.. Chesworth had seen the worst of the world and it's best. Through his beliefs compassion, love and hope have grown and not diminished.

I commend this collection of stories to everyone. They are wonderfully politically incorrect. They do not relate to the National Curriculum, Key Stage or S.A.T.'s but they will bring insight, calm. peace, hope and guidance for young people for their futures, like the butterfly story told at the funeral. I trust that all who read these stories will enjoy them as much as I have.

Steven Bowditch
Headmaster

INTRODUCTION

One of the great joys of my life has been in telling the boys and girls about Jesus and the Christian life, and especially to my eight grandchildren who have heard the enclosed stories many, many times. I have often been asked to publish them. Of course not all of them are original. I have chosen the best ones I have found and am grateful to the various publishers for their permission to reproduce the ones I have indicated.

I am indebted to the Epworth Press for allowing me permission to include several stories from Rita Snowden - H W Goldsack - Derrick Cuthbert - and George Fairfoot and to B. McCall Barbour for the Grasshopper Story. All the other tales are mine and ones given to me by friends.

I hope these stories from Tales To Tell will encourage Young People to follow the Master who was Himself the Master of the Art of Living.

DEDICATION

This book is dedicated to

Louise, Martyn, Andrew, Benjamin,
Joseph, Jennifer, Kingsley and Helen.

My Grandchildren.

OUR DOG GYP - A TRUE STORY

The Manse where we lived was huge. Six large bedrooms, no water laid on, a pump in the garden behind the manse, just a wooden toilet hut at the bottom of the garden, which accommodated two at a time and in winter it was dreadful. For a bath we had to pull an old zinc bath in front of the kitchen boiler and take as many buckets of hot water from it as you needed. In the garden, which was very big, were four old disused cottages which made a super playground., but they were not a little dangerous, and right in the middle of the garden was the biggest Apple Tree you've ever seen. At the far end of the garden was the hen-pen and beyond that a field with a very angry looking bull in it.

Father had twenty four Methodist Chapels to look after and he did this with the aid of a very old Douglas motor-bike. It had sit up and beg handlebars, a square petrol tank with the gear lever in the middle, a belt-drive and no kick-start. To start it you had to put it into gear then run with it till it engaged, and jump on. That was bad enough for the driver but the poor passenger had terrible problems repeating the process as the driver sped down the road.

One evening, father set off on his motorbike to go to a little Chapel called Magdalen Fen. It was a week-night Missionary meeting, an annual event when they had a Thanksgiving service and emptied the missionary boxes in which people had been collecting monies throughout the year. Now we had a lovely dog called

Gyp, a very important member of the family. Every time father was away at his Churches, Gyp would lie on a mat by the back door as if he was guarding the place and we were all very grateful, for we lived in a very isolated hamlet and in winter time it was dark and eerie.

This particular night, soon after father had gone, Gyp was missing. We all searched high and low but he was nowhere to be found. Believe it or not he turned up seven miles away at the little Chapel where father was preaching. He pushed open the door, walked down the aisle, went up into the pulpit and lay at father's feet the whole time he preached. At the end of the service they had tea and refreshments and emptied all the missionary boxes. They made a grand total of over £50, which was a lot of money in those days. The money was put into a leather bag and strapped onto the pillion of the motorbike. On the way home, travelling slowly so Gyp could follow, they had to travel through a thick wood, and halfway through it a man jumped out and accosted Dad. The man struggled to obtain the bag, a fight ensued, then, in the nick of time, up came Gyp snarling and biting the vagabond's legs. The man let go and fled and the money was all intact.

The dog never did that before nor since and somehow it spoke a lot to me of the Providence of God.

A PRAYER

Heavenly Father we are unworthy people, and there is not much that is very good about any of us. We ask forgiveness for all our mistakes.

Grant that we may be given the necessary help and guidance so that we can avoid the mistakes of life.

Bless those who are dear to us, especially any who are facing difficult problems.

Help us to know that in every situation we have to face we are never alone for You are always at hand to help us all.

Amen.

ARTHUR SMITH

A long time ago, there was a lad called Arthur Smith and all he wanted to be was a farmer. So, on leaving school, his father took him to the best farmer around and asked him to help make Arthur into a real good farmer.

Arthur worked very hard and his master was very pleased with him. In fact he grew to rely on Arthur very much and as the years went by Arthur was doing just about everything and his master less and less.

Then one day Arthur went round to his master's house, knocked on the door and told his master he wanted to talk. He was invited into the house, had a cup of tea, and in front of a magnificent farmhouse fire his master asked him what he wanted.

Arthur was very hesitant at first and very nervous, but eventually explained to his master that he wanted to leave. Having worked for his master for over seven years he felt the time had come when he ought to start on his own, with a farm of his own. He had thought long and hard about it and decided to go to Australia and try and make his fortune there. He was very sorry to leave for he had been very happy and had had a wonderful time, but he needed more money so that was what he intended to do.

His master was very dismayed. He had come to rely so much on Arthur but explained that he really could not afford to pay him any more, he would have to sell the farm. However he told Arthur he understood but would like him to work his week's notice and then come and see him before he left. Arthur did work his week's notice and then went to see his master again. He knocked on the door, the farmer took him inside and once again they had a cup of tea and a real good chat. They talked of all the wonderful times the had enjoyed together, of the bad times too and how much they would miss each other. Then, just as Arthur was about to leave, they shook hands, wished each other well, and his master pulled out of his pocket a letter and said 'Arthur. I want you to take this letter. It might prove helpful in days to come.' He took the letter and departed, feeling not a little sad.

Having got outside and on his way to Southampton with very little luggage indeed, he decided he had better read his letter. He was absolutely flabbergasted. In that letter his master had said all kinds of nice things about him. What a good worker he was, that he was completely honest and thoroughly reliable, how he would miss him etc. etc. but wished him well and hoped he would be very successful in Australia. The letter went on like that. He just couldn't believe that anyone should have such a good opinion of him as that. He put the letter carefully away and continued to Southampton.

There were thousands of people on board, many with friends and lots of luggage, but Arthur was all alone with hardly any luggage. However whenever he felt lonely he would pull out the letter and read it. He did it many times. When they had been out at sea for days he was still doing it and people began to notice this lonely young man always reading this letter. They thought of course that it must be something special, perhaps a love letter. Arthur never bothered what anyone thought. Whenever he felt like it he pulled out his letter and read it.

One day he was on the deck when suddenly the sun went in and the clouds lowered, the wind began to howl, the ship began to roll. Everyone disappeared into their cabins. All except Arthur, he just sat there, pulled out his letter and began to read it again. Then, all at once, a great gust of wind whipped the letter out of his hand, into the air and out to sea. He was frantic. He shouted and screamed at the top of his voice for them to STOP THE SHIP. He hung over the stern of the ship and watched his precious letter floating on the waves. 'STOP THE SHIP' he shouted again and again. The passengers thought he was going mad and sent for the Captain. He came running up on deck and tried to calm Arthur and eventually managed to persuade him to go with him to the Captain's Office where he would do something about it. The Captain took out a piece of paper and wrote on it these words: 'THIS IS TO CERTIFY THAT ARTHUR SMITH CAME ON BOARD WITH A GOOD CHARACTER BUT HE LOST IT IN A STORM !!!'

That letter was his certificate of character which we all have on leaving school, or in seeking a new job. It takes a lifetime to build your character but you can lose it in a moment, by telling a lie, or being unkind and dishonest.

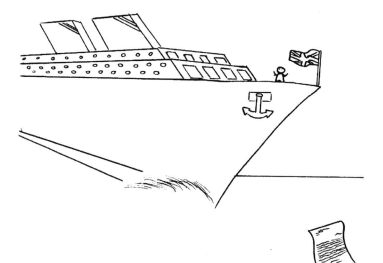

A PRAYER

Almighty God our Heavenly Father, we thank you for the privilege we have of living another day in this wonderful world in which we have been placed. A world of light and colour and constant excitement and adventure, a world of immense beauty.

Forgive us if we, in the hurly and burly of living sometimes forgot to be thankful and take for granted what we ought to take with gratitude.

Blessings we pray on all those, who through disability, are deprived of the enjoyment of your wonderful world.

THE PECULIAR HOUSE

Tom and Mary were invited, when the school holidays arrived, to go and visit their aunt who lived in a beautiful bungalow in the country and they were to go for three whole weeks. They were very excited, for they liked their aunt and they had never been away together before. They saved up all their pocket money and when the day finally arrived they were given their instructions about being good and polite etc. etc.

Their aunt was pleased to receive them and gave them a good welcome but she really wasn't used to children. The first few days were alright but the childrens nervous tension soon disappeared and they were flying about everywhere making far too much noise for the liking of their aunt. At the end of the first week she thought, 'However am I going to manage another day.' She was just about tearing her hair and she determined to do something about it.

It was breakfast time on the first day of the last week and she said to the children. 'I want you to go out and find a house. It is red on one side, green on the other, with a chimney on top and a star inside ..... and don't come back until you've found it !!!'. She said it with such emphasis that they knew she really meant it and she kept repeating it. She went on, 'you can take some pop, a package of sandwiches, but don't come back until you've found it'. The words were ringing in their ears as they walked down the garden path to start their search.

10

They looked at every house in the village. Some were red all round, some even had green roofs but whoever had heard of a house that was red on one side, green on the other, with a chimney on top and a star inside?

Without success they went on to the next village and the next and the next till it was well past dinnertime and Tom said to Mary, 'House or no house, I'm hungry. Let's eat'. They sat down on the roadside, had their sandwiches and drank their pop when suddenly Tom noticed a wood about a quarter of a mile away. 'That's it' he exclaimed. I'll bet it's in that wood'. They explored it thoroughly but there was no sign of what they were looking for. They trundled on until it was well past teatime and really getting late. They were sat on a farm gate feeling very sorry for themselves and a long way from home but not daring to return. Tom was hot and sticky, Mary's hair was bedraggled. Then the farmer's wife came out and asked what they were about. They told her of the house they had to find and without which they dare not return. 'I've lived here all my life' said the farmer's wife 'and have never seen any such house round here, but let's go and ask the farmer'. Inside the farmhouse they were given some cake and a glass of milk. Then the farmer came in and he was asked to help.

'Very well' he said to the children. 'Follow me'. He took them into the farmyard and said 'now look around and tell me if you can see what you are looking for here'. They could see nothing except the things you normally find in a farmyard. There was an old plough in one corner and some ducks waddling in a pond. 'Well, follow me' said the farmer and took them round the other side of the farm where all the barns were. 'Can you see anything here?' he said to the children. There were haylofts and ladders leading up to them. Bales of straw, a hen with her chickens, but certainly no house that was red on one side, green on the other with a chimney on top, and whoever heard of a house with a star inside? 'Right' said the farmer. 'Follow me' and he took them right round the other side of the farm. At the bottom of the farm was a large orchard and in the middle of the orchard they saw a large hut looking very green with age. They really thought they were getting warm but, no, it was not what they were looking for. The farmer said 'Are you sure you can't see what you want, because I think you are really blind'. He lifted up his arm and plucked an apple from the tree and said to them. 'Here it is - an apple. It's red on one side, green on the other and this is your chimney on top', pointing to the stalk. Then Tom whispered to Mary and the farmer said 'What did you say?' 'Well,' said Tom. 'What about the star inside?' 'You watch' said the farmer and promptly took out his pen knife. He placed the apple on its side and cut it through the middle and where the pippins meet it showed the perfect shape of a star !!!

A star figures a lot in the life of Jesus. The Wise Men and Shepherds were guided to the Bethlehem crib by a star. Jesus was often referred to as The Bright and Morning Star.

One day you will read Bunyan's Pilgrim's Progress and it starts out by describing the Pilgrim setting out with a load on his back to go to the Celestial City. He doesn't know the direction to take and asks a traveller who says to him 'Can you seen yonder wicket gate?' The pilgrim looks, but shakes his head. He can't see it. 'Well' said the traveller, 'can you see yonder shining star?' The pilgrim looks up and says 'Yes, I think I can'. 'Right' says the traveller, keep that star right in the centre of you eye and it will bring you to the wicket gate'.

We have to keep God right in the centre of our lives and He will bring us to where He wants us to be. He has a special job for you to do and a special job for me to do that no one else can do quite so well as we can.

A PRAYER

Grant Heavenly Father that we may ever become more sensitive to Spiritual things.

It is so easy for us, because of the sheer joy of living, to forget the author of our happiness and to become careless in spiritual things. Help us never to become selfish and so full of our own affairs as to forget the needs of others.

We remember before you all those who are sick or in troubled circumstances and commend them to your care and keeping.

THE HOLIDAY SURPRISE

The two teenage boys, who had been school friends for a long time, decided to go on holiday together. They were not rich enough to go abroad or even to the local seaside resort. The very best would be a hiking holiday. So they made their plans and got ready, taking only what they could fit into a back pack to be carried on their backs, including of course the tent they would need to sleep in.

The day arrived and they set off. It was raining, but they thought it will soon stop, it can't go on for ever. However it did rain quite heavily all day and all the next day too. In fact it never stopped raining all that week, all day and all night. Halfway through the second week they were still walking and it was still raining. Every step they took the water squelched in their boots and they were thoroughly miserable.

Tom said to his friend Bill, 'We really can't go on like this. We'd better call it off and go home'. 'Tell you what' said Tom. 'We'll go as far as the next town and if it is still raining we will give it up and go home'. 'O.K.' said Bill. 'we'll do just that'.

When they did arrived at the next town it was still raining but there was great excitement, and the place was packed with people everywhere. It didn't take them long to find out that it was the annual holidays, and all kind of things were happening. There was the annual Circus on the village green, in the biggest tent you have ever seen, and the local Fayre with the coconut shying, pot shooting, roundabouts etc. 'I think we'll stay here tonight' said Tom and Bill agreed. So off they went to the Fayre and did they enjoy themselves? They certainly did!!

It was after midnight and it was still raining. The tent was too wet to use, and they were sheltering in a shop doorway. They tried everywhere to get accommodation for the night but every place they tried said 'Sorry. Full up'. So many people had descended on the little town. Then across the road they noticed a light in a doorway. They dashed across and knocked on the door. A little old lady from inside looked at them through the glass panel and shook her head, telling them she too had no room but they continued pleading with her. She opened the door to let them in to shelter from the rain, and again she explained she had no room. They looked so pitiful that she relented and said 'You can stay in the kitchen, and in the next room you can sleep on the floor. I'll bring you some blankets. At least you'll be out of the rain. There is no light in there - you'll just have to manage'.

There was a fire in the kitchen so they warmed themselves. She made them a cup of tea and bid them goodnight and went to bed.

After a while they took the blankets and tried to make their beds on the floor in the dark. They found it most difficult as they weren't used to making beds, and they were up and down like a cat at a fayre. First Tom's feet stuck through the bottom then Bill had a draught down his back. Then Tom felt some stone under his blanket and so it went on. Eventually Bill said 'This is hopeless'. He felt in his pocket and produced a box of matches, and searching around in the dark with the aid of his matches, he stumbled across a perfectly good mattress. 'Hey Tom' he said. 'Look what I've found. I thought she said she had no bed'. But, without trying to work it out, they both took their blankets, spread them on the mattress and fell fast asleep. Next morning when they woke up they were horrified and so embarrassed. There were crowds of people laughing their heads off and looking at them. THEY WERE IN A SHOP WINDOW!!!

Christians are always in a shop window! People make up their minds about our Master by what they see of Him in us.

A PRAYER

Help us dear Lord to learn how to be still and quiet so that even though the noises of life are very distracting we can still hear the 'still small voice', speaking directly to us through our conscience - our reading - our friends. Keep us sensitive spiritually so that we can receive guidance and direction and so fulfil whatever is your will and purpose in our life.

THE BABY JESUS AND PRESENTS

When the Baby Jesus was born in Bethlehem, there was a great deal of fuss and excitement everywhere. It was the time of the Passover and everyone was very busy. As there was no accommodation for Joseph and Mary they had to stay in a stable with all the cattle around them and that was where Jesus was born.

Right in the corner of the stable, underneath some straw, so the story goes, was a little caterpillar. It dare not come out for fear of being trodden on so it just kept poking its head out to have a look. It realised it must be a very important baby as everybody was bringing presents and there were lots of people coming and going. When eventually things quietened down and people had stopped coming, the little caterpillar thought to itself, 'I wish I had a present to give to the little baby'. Then it noticed, right across the other side of the stable was an ivy leaf. Very slowly and very quietly it slid across the stable floor and picked up the ivy leaf and carried it to the stall where the Baby Jesus was lying in a manger cradle, fast asleep. He was all tightly bound as was the custom in eastern countries.

The caterpillar climbed up the wooden pillar to the manger cradle, still with the ivy leaf in its mouth, and when it got right to the top, it stopped and had a real good look at the lovely little Baby Jesus. It stayed there quite a while and then very slowly it crawled down into the manger and planted the ivy leaf right in the centre of the baby Jesus' chest. Again it stayed to have yet another good look before it turned away to go back to its corner in the stable and just as it turned the Baby Jesus roused, pulled His little hand out of His clothes and just touched the caterpillar and suddenly it GLOWED all over and ever since has been called the Glow Worm!!!

It's a lovely story but only a story. It reminds me, however, that everything that Jesus touched then and since has always been transformed. He Himself was called The Light of the World.

A PRAYER

Forgive us Heavenly Father if we have been guilty of ever being less than our best. The high standard of Christian living is very demanding and often we fail to maintain that standard.

If we have been unkind in things we have said, or unjust in things we have done, hurtful in our dealings with others - forgive us. Help us to do better and be a shining example to all about us, as to what a Christian should be. Grant that people seeing us will want to know You.

ON BEING LOCKED OUT

Being a Minister of religion is a busy life, and being a Minister's wife is also a very demanding job.

One day, a certain Minister's wife had to go to a very important meeting some miles away and she gave instructions to her husband to do some shopping for her whilst she was away. She gave him the list of things she required, mainly from the grocers shop round the corner, and she said she would be back round 5 p.m. but as that would be too late to receive the children from school, would he be sure to be at home when they came in. She disappeared on the local bus to the Church where her meeting was to be held.

The Minister was very busy that day, answering the telephone and writing letters, making sermons etc. He also had several visits to make and it was while he was out visiting an old lady he glanced at his watch and was horrified to discover that he should be at home for the children. He had not got the groceries either. He literally flew home in his car, got the groceries, dashed to the house. The children hadn't arrived, which was such a relief then he realised that he had locked himself out !!! What a fool you feel when that happens. He looked round the house for some means of entrance but alas there seemed no way in at all. Then he noticed the only window unlocked was at the back of the Manse in an upstairs bedroom.

Across the road some workmen were making extensive alterations to a very big house owned by a very wealthy man who went to his Church. He was away on holiday but the workmen had left a big ladder on the ground. Just what he was looking for, so he 'borrowed' it, took it to the back bedroom window and began to climb. He hated heights and with every step his tummy turned over, but eventually he got off the heaving ladder, cocked his leg over the windowsil he'd managed to open and got inside. Quickly he ran downstairs, out through the front door, and ran to the back of the house and putting his hand in his inside pocket found the very key he wanted!!! He had all he needed all the time to get into the house.

Life is just like that. God has given us a wonderful world to live in, and a wonderful body to relate to that world. In fact He has given us everything we shall ever need to live the life He wanted us to live. He even has a special job for us to do that no one else can do as well as we can.

A PRAYER

We know Heavenly Father because of the Crucifixion and the teachings of Our Lord how important we are to You. Such love we can never understand or deserve, but we are truly grateful. We are especially grateful when we remember that even when we do not respond to that call and our lives turn away from You - You never ever desert us.

Forgive us we pray for all our foolish ways and restore within us the Spirit of true love.

CHECK-MATE

It is not generally known that the famous artist, Holman Hunt, renowned for his portrait of Jesus standing at the door, His hand on the latch and waiting for someone from inside to respond to His knocking, and open it from the inside, also painted many other wonderful pictures.

One was of a young boy playing a game of Chess with the Devil. The pieces were all laid out on the chess board, the game had obviously been in progress some time, then there was a great big grin on the horrible face of the Devil as he thought he had trapped the young boy into submission, and written large across the picture were the words CHECK-MATE!!!

A friend, studying the picture for a while, turned to the owner of the picture and said 'But it isn't true - if the boy made this particular move', pointing to the pieces on the board, 'from here to there, there is a way out and he's not defeated'.

There are lots and lots of people in the world who have written CHECK-MATE across their lives, and given up all hope of success, but with Jesus there is always a way out. - It is called forgiveness.

A PRAYER

Lord Jesus - teach us how to be steadfast in all we do, diligent in our work, patient in our dealings with other people.

Help us always to be truthful and forgiving and altogether living examples of what a Christian ought to be.

Give strength and courage to all these who are trying to live the Christian life, and especially those who facing adversity, are tempted to discard their Faith. Grant that those with question marks raised in their hearts may find them answered in such a way that they will understand that your plan for their life has not been discarded.

JOHNNY'S BIG SURPRISE

One day Johnny came down for breakfast and waited for his mother to arrive. He was a very polite boy and very well mannered. To his surprise, when she did arrive, she was all dressed up in her Sunday best clothes, she was also a little flustered as though she was excited and not a little nervous. He was far too polite to ask questions but during the course of having breakfast Johnny's mother said to him 'I'm going out this morning and I want you to be a good boy and look after things for me. I won't be very long, about three quarters of an hour, but I have a very important matter to attend to. Whilst I'm away I would like you to see to the baby, she shouldn't be any trouble, she's fed and asleep. You can clear the table and wash the dishes, chop some firewood and generally keep an eye on things till I return, and if you're very good and do all these things, when I return I'll give you an extra 50p to your pocket money'.

Johnny was delighted and couldn't wait for her to go. He couldn't help wondering what his mother was up to, but was too polite to ask. She put on her best coat, her best gloves, picked up her new handbag and disappeared out of the front door. Johnny glanced back. The baby was alright so he thought he would just look in which direction she went. She went down the garden path, out of the gate, turned left, passing in front of the house and disappeared round a corner. Wherever could she be going, he thought to himself? By this time he had forgotten he had a baby to look after and jobs to do and followed his mother down into the village. He continued to follow. She stopped and looked in almost every shop, never went in any of them, just looked. He kept a respectable distance away just so she wouldn't see him. When she got to the end of the only row of shops the village had, she turned left and began walking up a rather steep hill, halfway up this hill on the right hand side was a high wall which surrounded a very large house. In the middle of this wall was a wooden door. She opened it, closed it and disappeared inside.

Johnny thought 'I wonder why she's gone in there?' He looked at the wall, it was high and he was only quite small, but he shinned up it quickly and thought to himself as he hung on with both hands. Now what's she doing? In front of the big house was a very big lawn and in the middle of the lawn, a table around which were several people, including Johnny's mother. They were chatting and drinking tea. Suddenly they would all get up, move around and sit down again. They did it several times, and there was a little dog there having a wonderful time. They seemed to be having a sort of little tea party because they were constantly pouring out cups of tea. They would pour out a cup., have a sip, stand up, move around, then sit down again for another drink. He was greatly puzzled and confused. Suddenly he remembered his mother said she wouldn't be long and he'd all those jobs to do.

He slid down the wall, and flew home as fast as his little legs could carry him. He was sure there would be trouble. The house on fire? or the baby crying it's head off? But when he got there all was quiet and the baby was still fast asleep. Very quickly he whipped round the house, did all the jobs his mother mentioned and he had no sooner finished than in walked his mother. 'Everything all right Johnny?' enquired his mother. 'Yes mother' he replied. 'The baby's still fast asleep and I've done all the jobs you mentioned'. 'Good boy'. She went to her purse, took out a 50p piece and believe it or not he took it.

Nothing else happened for about three weeks and Johnny had forgotten all about the whole matter. Sitting down to breakfast the postman arrived. He knocked on the door which wasn't usual. He handed Johnny a large thin package for which he had to sign, so he knew it must be important. At that moment his mother came downstairs all flushed and excited and demanded the package. It was really a sort of large thin cardboard box. She took ages to get into it, tore off the paper and the sellotape, then on this box was a lid which she removed and inside the box was a lot of tissue paper. She removed that and found a large folder. She opened that and what do you think? Inside the folder was the most beautiful picture of Johnny's mother you could ever wish to see... and at the back of the picture there was a wall, and hanging on to the wall was Little Johnny!!!

A text in the Bible says: 'Be sure your sins will find you out'.

A PRAYER

Eternal God our Heavenly Father. If I have been selfish today, thinking only of myself and forgetting the needs of others - Forgive me. We live in a world of hustle and bustle, everyone striving for what they want, even at the expense of others no matter what the cost.

Help me to be still and quiet and listen to what You are trying to say to me and make me sensitive enough in spiritual things to be able to hear and understand.

THE PROMISE

The Minister had just left the Church he had been serving for five years in order to go and be a Minister at another one in St Annes. The people were sorry to see him go and he was even more sorry to leave them. However, the new friends at St Annes gave him and his family a wonderful welcome and they soon began to feel at home.

After some weeks he was invited back to his old Church to preach. He set off early, in a very little car he had acquired, the very smallest car ever made. Do you know what make it was? A baby FIAT. It didn't run very well and kept stopping. That was why he had to set off really early even though he didn't have very far to go. All went well until halfway down a long straight road, there was an almighty Bang, clouds of smoke and the car stopped. He lifted the bonnet, tried to look intelligent, touched this and tickled that, but nothing happened. Then a big car drew up behind him. The driver a man, well dressed said 'Padre are you in trouble and can I help?' 'I wish you could' he said 'I'm going to be late for my preaching appointment'. He too looked under the bonnet and tried to look intelligent, touched this and tickled that, but nothing happened. 'Sorry' said he 'but I cannot help and will be late for my preaching appointment, because I'm a preacher too. Sorry I must go'. So off he went. Almost in despair the Minister waited for a miracle. Sure enough a van pulled up painted all yellow and black. A man in Khaki uniform emerged and said 'Hello Padre. Are you in trouble?' 'Not half' said the Minister. 'I am going to be very late for my appointment unless you can help me'. 'I'll try' he said.

Do you know who he was? Yes, of course, he was from the A.A.

'By the way' said the A.A. man. 'Are you in the A.A.?' 'No, I'm afraid I'm not'. 'Well you very soon will be' said the A.A. man and he promptly produced a large form, and gave it to the minister. This form said that in future if there was ever any trouble again with the car they promised always to come out and help. He duly signed on the dotted line and ever since has been in the A.A.

'It was only a bit of paper like this one', the minister said, which he tore up in front of them, but he kept the original because it contained a promise.

'Do you know what this is?' The Minister held up before them a £10 pound note. Many of the children immediately shouted out what it was. The minister then said. 'Do you know what it says on a £10 pound note'. 'I PROMISE TO PAY THE BEARER ON DEMAND THE SUM OF £10'. 'It's only a bit of paper'. He tore it in half , crumpled it up in his hand and made as though he was going to throw it to any of them who wanted it. Of course all stood up ready to catch it. But he didn't throw it, as he said he had borrowed it from his wife and she wanted it back, but it was important because it contained a Promise.

'Do you know what this is?' he said holding up another large document. 'I'll tell you. It's from the PRUDENTIAL. It's an insurance policy which my wife has taken out on my life. It says when I die she will get a lot of money. It's only a piece of paper. I could tear it up and throw it away but I won't, because it contains a very important promise and if they don't keep their promise, I shall be very cross!!!!'

'Do you know what this is? Be careful because showing it one day to some children, one little boy shouted out 'Sir. It's your PENSION BOOK'. 'No' said the Minister . 'It's my cheque book. Now if I owed your father £1,000 and I'm glad I don't, I would write out one of these cheques and he would take it to his bank to cash it. If there was only 2p in my bank he wouldn't get his money and be very shocked and I would be breaking my Promise'.

'Do you know what this is?' 'Yes' he said it's the Bible. Do you know that on almost every page there are wonderful promises made by God to all of us. Can you remember any of them? THE RAINBOW - God's promise never to flood the whole earth ever again. John 14. God's promise of ETERNAL LIFE to all who follow Him. There are loads and loads of them. But for all the notice many people take of the Bible it might just as well not exist. God never, never breaks His promises. If He did, as the Harvest time tells us, we should all die very quickly. Always remember to Keep Your Promises, especially to God.

HYMN AS A PRAYER

It is a thing most wonderful,
　　　Almost too wonderful to be,
That God's own Son should come from heaven
　　　And die to save a child like me.

And yet I know that it is true;
　　　He came to this poor world below,
And wept, and toiled, and mourned, and died,
　　　Only because He loved me so.

I cannot tell how He could love
　　　A child so weak and prone to sin;
His love must be most wonderful,
　　　If He could die my love to win.

It is most wonderful to know
　　　His love for me so free and sure;
But 'tis more wonderful to see
　　　My love for Him so faint and poor.

And yet I want to love Thee, Lord;
　　　O light the flame within my heart,
And I will love Thee more and more,
　　　Until I see Thee as Thou art.

THE RUNAWAY SLAVE

The Bible is full of really super stories. Let me tell you of one you will find between the New Testament Books of Hebrew and Titus.

There was a very wealthy man, probably a gentleman farmer whose name was Philemon. He had many servants and slaves who worked for him. He was a tough character and made them work extremely hard and long hours. One day he is walking down the road, probably towards Caperniaum, and sees in the distance a group of people all listening to a very little man on a box, speaking to them. He was just out for a stroll but as he had nothing better to do that afternoon he joined the crowd to hear what the man was saying. It turned out to be Paul, the man who was converted on the Damascus road and was now one of the main leaders of the Christian movement. He was telling very vividly the wonderful story of Jesus , how He was crucified, which everyone of course knew, but that He was not dead as everyone thought, He had risen from the grave and was gloriously alive and he could prove it to them as a number of them had actually seen and spoken to Jesus.

Philemon was not a particularly religious man but of course, like everyone else, he had heard of Jesus and the amazing things He had done and also like everyone else knew He had been crucified. He listened carefully and became more and more interested until at the end, like a lot of others, he too became thoroughly convinced and a completely changed man, so, much so that he went home and began to lead an altogether different life. He began to treat all his servants and slaves as though they were his best friends. They were completely stunned, and you can imagine the sort of comments they made to each other. Some said 'Oh it's just a flash in the pan, tomorrow he'll be up to his old tricks again, you just see'. Others said 'He's gone mad'. One of them, called Onesimus, was more sceptical than the rest but kept quiet, secretly he had decided this was his golden opportunity. He was certain the mood would pass and Philemon would revert to his old ways. He waited several days and Philemon was still as nice as ever. Then at last it came, the chance to escape. First he broke into his master's house, robbed him of a considerable amount of money then he fled.

For a time all went well. He had plenty of money and therefore lots of friends and he lived a life of luxury for quite a while. But the inevitable day came when Onesimus had spent his last, began to be in debt to his friends, his landlady and lots of others. Now that his money was gone his friends soon disappeared. He was reduced to rags and tatters, no food, no money and no friends. In this wretched state he began to think of his old life as a slave, even that was better than what he had now. At least his bread and butter was sure and he had a roof over his head. He began to think of the one who converted his master. Paul. There and then he made up his mind to go and see Paul, tell him the whole miserable story and throw himself on his mercy. He couldn't go back to Philemon because the Roman law said that if a servant deserted a master he was punishable by death, so Paul was the only answer.

We see Onesimus now in all his rags making his way to the house where Paul lived. Paul was a prisoner of Rome but allowed to live in his own house, what we today would refer to as being under 'open arrest'. He could go anywhere but only if accompanied by a Roman soldier. In that sense he was a prisoner.

Onesimus knocked at the door and this very little man called Paul opened the door. Onesimus told him his story and Paul listened. He invited Onesimus into the house and asked him some questions. 'When did you last eat?' Well he hadn't had a decent meal for ages so Paul gave him something to eat. 'Are those the only clothes you have?' 'Yes indeed'. They were all ragged and torn so Paul found his some better clothes and he was most grateful. 'Where did you sleep last night?' Well, for many nights he had slept rough, in hedge bottoms etc. so Paul said that he could stay with him that night. He did and the next and the next and the next night. In fact he stayed a lot of nights and a certain bond of friendship grew up between Paul and Onesimus.

One day, Paul realising that the Roman law also said that if someone kept another's slave in hiding he also was punishable by death, decided he had to talk with Onesimus. He talked to Onesimus about the great change that came to his master, Philemon. Told him the same story that Philemon had heard in the marketplace with all the other people and at the end Onesimus, like his master, also became a changed man. 'Now' said Paul to Onesimus . 'You don't belong to me and you must go back to your master'. You can almost hear Onesimus crying out 'NO. NEVER - HE'LL KILL ME'. 'Don't worry' said Paul. 'I'll write you a letter and you'll have nothing to fear'. He took out his pen and a sheet of paper and he wrote the beautiful letter we have in the Bible in which he says:

'I thank God for you every day Philemon for I have heard of your love and Faith which you have towards the Lord Jesus. I am writing to you on behalf of my friend, Onesimus, who I have in my house and who was in times past unprofitable to you, and to me, but is now profitable to us both. I am sending him back to you and I want you to receive him, not now as a slave but as a brother beloved, especially to me. I am writing to you knowing that you will do more than I say and if he has robbed you or oweth you ought, put it on my account and when I come to see you I'll repay it. Remember Philemon you owe your own self to me in the Christian life. Soon I hope to come and see you so prepare for me a lodging and give my greeting to the friends in your area'. He signed himself Paul and handed the letter to Onesimus, sent him back to his master. They became reconciled and all was well again.

Here you have a perfect picture of the Wheel of Christianity turning full circle.

A PRAYER

We are grateful Heavenly Father for the wonderful life we have been given and for the sheer joy of living. Our health and strength, our ability to stand on our own two feet, to be able to think and make decisions.

For all the beauty of nature that surrounds us and the exciting adventures presented to us as each day comes and goes.

We remember before you all those throughout the World who, because of disability, are unable, through no fault of their own, to enjoy the pleasures of life bestowed upon all of us.

Amen.

THE PEDLAR - A TRUE STORY

Many years ago before the great fire of London, there lived in the little market town of Swaffham in Norfolk, a Pedlar. He was a well known figure and he went from house to house selling his wares. Pins, pocket knives, buttons, almost anything you wanted he would have it or get it. He carried a bag on his back, had a walking stick and a dog who followed him everywhere.

One night, when he went to bed, he had a dream. He dreamt that if he went to London Town and stood on London Bridge, something good would happen to him. It was so vivid that he couldn't get it out of his mind. He thought about it long and hard. Then he said to his dog 'Shall we go and see?' The dog barked, as though to say 'Yes', so he decided to go. London was a long way away, about 150 miles at least.

They set off and walked as far as they could every day and eventually arrived in London. They were very tired and had sore feet but soon forgot their troubles as they looked at all the wonderful things in London. The big buildings, the huge bridges and hundreds of shops and offices. They made their way to London Bridge and in those days there were shops on the bridge.

They stayed there all day and saw thousands of people passing backwards and forwards but absolutely nothing happened, and no one spoke to them. Just as they were about to give up and turn for home a man from the Butchers shop went over to them and said 'What are you up to? I've been watching you all day, walking backwards and forwards - do you want something?' The Pedlar explained all about his dream and that if he came to London Bridge something good would happen to him but he said 'It was only a dream, I suppose. I was foolish to come'. The Butcher burst out laughing and kept on laughing. He said to the Pedlar 'You'll not believe this, but last night I also had a dream. I dreamt that in a place called Swaffham in Norfolk there was a house with a garden. In the middle of which was a very big apple tree and underneath this apple tree buried in the ground, was a pot of gold but it was only a dream. Whoever heard of such a thing?' He went back to his shop laughing his head off.

The Pedlar was astounded, he had an apple tree at home. Such a coincidence! He really couldn't believe it, but he turned for home, with his knapsack on his back, his walking stick and his little dog. They went as fast as they possibly could all the way back to Swaffham. Eventually they arrived and though they were so tired with sore feet, they went straight to the apple tree and dug and dug and dug and sure enough they came across a mug full of gold coins. The Pedlar was elated. He was suddenly a very rich man. He took the coins and hid them in his house and he didn't tell a soul of his good fortune.

One day, the local school master came to see him. The Pedlar had noticed that on the mug was some writing in Latin which he couldn't understand, so without telling the school master about his gold coins, asked him if he could interpret it for him. The school master looked at it and said 'It says' underneath me there is another one twice as big!' As soon as the school master had gone he got his spade and dug and dug deep down below the tree and again he found a mug, twice as big and full of beautiful gold coins. Now he was very, very rich.

Some time passed and the local Vicar had to appeal to his congregation for financial help to repair the Church roof. The Pedlar thought he ought to come clean and for the first time tell the Vicar the truth of his new-found wealth. He gave the Vicar enough money to repair the roof, 200 gold sovereigns, and also enough to build some new school buildings and money for future years. Eventually the Pedlar died. The Vicar and all the people decided they ought to do something to perpetuate the memory of the Pedlar so they engaged a wood carver to carve the figure of Pedlar John and his little dog on the ends of the pews in the Church where he worshipped. If you go there you can see them for yourself, they are still there.

The name of the pedlar was John Chapman and he lived in the reign of King Henry the Seventh.

A PRAYER

Almighty God our Heavenly Father, we know You are more ready to hear our Prayers than we are to pray. Forgive us if in the busy life we live, we sometimes forget to communicate with You.

We realise that apart from You we can do nothing, and achieve nothing, and indeed we depend upon You for the very breath we breathe.

Help us to live our life sensibly and well knowing that we are always living in Your presence.

THE ISLAND WITH ONE TOP-HAT

How would you like to live on an island where there are no shops, no roads, no policemen, no cars or buses, and where no one has any money? An island where there is only one wedding ring and only one top-hat, which are borrowed by each bride and bridegroom in turn whenever a wedding takes place? There is such an island, and British people have been living on it for over 170 years. Its name is Tristan da Cunha, and it is rightly called the loneliest island in the world, for it lies in the middle of the South Atlantic so far away from anywhere, even the ordinary shipping routes, that the inhabitants count themselves lucky if they see a ship once a year.

The name of the settlement where the people live is Edinburgh, and that name is enough to tell you that the colony was founded by a Scot. A certain William Glass, who had served in the garrison stationed on the island at the time of Napoleon's defeat and whose wife, a Creole lady, had found it difficult to settle in Edinburgh, Scotland, went out to Tristan da Cunha in 1821, taking some of his friends with him. In the houses left standing by the garrison when it was withdrawn they made their homes. That was the beginning of the colony, and there are now over two hundred people living in it. But the only surnames on the island are the names of the original settlers and the islanders still sing Scottish songs and dance Highland dances.

Life is very simple on Tristan, as you can guess. Farming, fishing and hunting are the occupations of the people, and their food consists mainly of potatoes, fish and milk. Occasionally a ship will visit the island, bringing mail, sugar, tea, soap, flour, tools and other things which the islanders cannot produce for themselves. It is a hard life, but a healthy one, and everyone goes to church. The Rev. A G Partridge, who was for some years their minister, has told how, in addition to the regular services, they would all gather in the church for a service if the day was too stormy for outdoor work. Mr Partridge, by the way, was not only their minister, but teacher, magistrate, dentist and doctor as well! In three years he had only three cases of wrong-doings to deal with - trivial thefts which were soon detected and punished - and this shows that the people of Tristan live their religion as well as profess it.

And so we may say that although on Tristan da Cunha they lack many of the things which we take for granted, they are rich in honesty, in kindness and in friendship. It is this that makes the islanders so anxious to go on living there. If the island did possess roads and shops and fine houses; if everybody had a wedding ring and lots of other rings besides; if every man has a different top-hat for each day of the week and a fine motor car to ride in; if they had every luxury that you can think of, and at the same time there was no honesty and no spark of kindness among them; if they were entirely selfish and had no thought for their duty to others and to God, then Tristan would not only be the loneliest island, it would be the world's worst island, and nobody in his senses would dream of living there.

There are lots of material things we can do without. The people of Tristan have known this for many years, but it has taken a war to make some of us over here understand it. Our happiness does not depend upon top-hats, upon rich food and motor cars. It depends upon spiritual things. If we love God and worship Him and love our neighbour and help him, then whatever else we may lack, we are rich indeed.

A PRAYER

Grant O Heavenly Father to those who suffer physical and spiritual ill health the recovery they seek.

Jesus gave healing to many suffering physically and spiritually and we know 'Your touch has still its ancient Power'.

Give to our Doctors, Nurses, Scientists and all who seek to help those who suffer, the wisdom and learning required to banish all disease.

Hear our Prayer and let our cry come unto You O Lord.

Amen.

THE GRASSHOPPER THAT
SAVED A BOY'S LIFE

One summer's day, a young boy, on his way home from school along a country lane, enjoyed himself chasing the birds and the butterflies, until he startled a grasshopper. He then began chasing it, and my, how that grasshopper could jump! To escape the boy, it at last jumped over a fence, whereupon the boy followed. But that was as far as the chase went for there, on the ground on the other side of the fence, lay a bundle of clothes, cosily covering the form of a baby boy, whose sweet, innocent face and lovely eyes at once attracted him. Seeing no one around, and feeling that it was unsafe to leave the little one lying there, he decided that the best thing to do was to take it home to his mother. Having come to this decision, he gathered the little bundle into his arms and made for home.

The little unwanted baby was nameless. No one ever knew who was its mother or where it had come from. And so this little baby boy was taken into this new home and cared for a member of the family.

You might not expect much from a boy who had received such a strange start in life, and yet this boy grew up to be a remarkably clever man and , what is more important still, an exceedingly good man. He became rich and powerful, and served his country so well that he was knighted, and is known in history by the honourable name of Sir Thomas Gresham.

In the heart of the city of London there is an imposing building called the Royal Exchange. It was built in honour of Sir Thomas Gresham and at the top of this building you will see, not a rooster or a cross, but a grasshopper. That grasshopper still tells the story of how a grasshopper was used by God to guide the footsteps of a little schoolboy in the rescue of a little abandoned child.

There is a story in the Bible about a little baby boy who was found in a basket by the riverside. A princess found him. adopted him as her own, and had him brought up in the palace in all the wealth and culture of Egypt. No one, apart from God, ever knew that Moses was destined to become a prince in Egypt, and later on the greatest leader and law-giver this world has ever known.

God has a wonderful way of caring for little children. And God loves and cares for you. God needs you and perhaps has some wonderful work for you to do which no one can do but you. And one day if you keep close to Him, God will make that work plain and clear to you.

A PRAYER

O God, we are grateful to you for revealing to us the Wonder of your Love, Care and Goodness - and for the knowledge that through life is constantly changing - You do not change.

When we have to pass through difficult times and life's shadows close in upon us, help us still to be able to feel the touch of your Hand upon ours - leading us on to the fulfilment of our appointed task.

Turn our Darkness into Light we pray.

Through Jesus Christ Our Lord.

Amen.

THE UNION JACK
FOR A SCOUT PARADE

I intend to take a text for this talk, not from the Bible (I will give you that at the close), but from our national life. I wish to speak about the flag, which is the emblem of our country, and which is the chief of the colours of your Group. We will not trouble about the history of the Union Jack and the flag of which it is composed; you learn about that in day school. Let us rather take the colours of the Union Jack, the red, the white, the blue; and let them remind us of three virtues of a good scout and a good Christian. But first, a story.

During the Coronation celebrations, a B.B.C. Announcer was touring Scotland. He gave an account of his experiences over the radio the same evening, and told of the many flags which he had seen, and of the rejoicing which had been made. Outside one house, among the decorations, had been placed some flags, the meaning of which had apparently not been understood. According to the International Code of Shipping the message read as follows: 'Keep away; yellow fever on board!' Flags are usually symbols. They are messages. Let us then, take the three colours of the Union Jack, and let them stand for virtues. I will illustrate each one from life.

RED

The first colour in the Union Jack is red. What does that stand for? Yes: red stands for danger. That will scarcely suit my purpose: scouts must not be dangerous!

They should be just the reverse; they should be protectors from danger. But to stand in the way of danger and protect others will mean .... what? Courage. Let red stand for courage.

Now I expect you already know there are two kinds of courage. There is physical courage, and there is also moral courage. And here is my first story to illustrate both kinds.

Dr. Waterhouse tells how once he was travelling on a train between London and a suburban station. It so happened that on the same train were two Arabs. All went well until just near the destination. Then, with all the suddenness of the southern temperament, the two men quarrelled. Words gave way to blows, and blows to worse. One man took from his pocket a knife, opened it, and attacked his one-time friend. At this moment the train was pulling up at the platform, and the man who was being attacked opened the door, sprang out, and went running up the platform with his opponent pursuing him. Now it so happened that on the same platform was a young and alert porter who had noticed the commotion. Very quickly he decided what to do. He let the first man pass him by, but as the second came near, the porter put out his foot, tripped him up, sprang upon him, gripped his hand, turned it, and out the knife fell harmlessly on to the station platform. The man was arrested and taken to prison. Next day he was charged with causing a breach of the peace, and was duly sentenced. When the case was finished the magistrate turned to the young porter who was in court giving evidence, and congratulated him on his courage. This is what the young man said: 'It's no credit to me, sir. Ever since I have been on the railway I have prayed each morning that I might be able to do my duty.' That porter showed both kinds of courage: physical courage by which he captured the prisoner, but also that greater and more difficult moral courage, by which, in a court of law he was not ashamed to confess his faith in God.

What does your scout Law say? 'A scout smiles and whistles under all circumstances.' To do that will often demand courage of the highest type.

What would'st thou trembling soul?
Strength for the fight:
Strength for this fiery war
That we call life.
Courage thou trembling soul;
Wounds thou must bear:

But thou shalt find a strength
Will match despair -
Within thy Saviour's heart,
Seek for it there.

Red stands for courage, moral even more than physical.

WHITE

The second colour in the Union Jack is white. Now white stands only for one thing, and that is purity. 'A scout is clean in thought, word and deed.' Here is my second story.

The Rev. Henry Howard, of Australia, used to tell how once he tried to prepare a sermon on those words of Jesus which often come to mind when we think of purity. 'Blessed are the pure in heart for they shall see God'. The minister began his preparation, and had proceeded some little way, when he came to a full stop! He thought and puzzled, but the ideas simply would not come, and he began to feel he would have to abandon the sermon. Then he looked up and noticed his telephone on the table, and he had an inspiration. In the same town there lived an eye specialist - a friend of the minister's. So he rang him up on the 'phone and asked if there was a disease of the heart that affected the eyesight'

'Yes', came the answer, 'there certainly is'.

'Tell me about it, will you?'

So, very briefly, the specialist described this complaint. He told how the heart being diseased affected the bloodstream; this, in turn, reached the eyes, which became bloodshot. 'If the patient is not cured,' he said, 'the sight may be lost for good.'

'What is the name of the complaint?' asked Mr Howard.

The doctor gave a long Latin name, the technical name. Then he said, 'We have a nickname for this disease. Commonly we call it a 'dirty heart'.

That is very significant, scouts. There is a physical disease of the heart leading to blindness. There is also a spiritual and moral disease that leads to spiritual blindness. That is one reason why Jesus said 'Blessed are the pure in heart for they shall see God.' A clean heart gives clear vision.

> When evil thoughts molest,
> With this I shield my breast -
> May Jesus Christ be praised!

White stands for purity.

BLUE

The third colour is blue. What shall we make blue stand for? We sometimes say 'True blue'. It might mean truth. Or, again, we speak of 'a bolt from the blue'. We might make blue stand for originality! It might in fact, stand for almost anything. Let me, therefore, suggest that it symbolises forgiveness - a spirit, a temper, of which the whole world stands greatly in need. What is your fifth law? 'A scout is a friend to all and a brother to every other scout.' You will never be a good friend, and certainly not a good brother, unless you can forgive. A Frenchman, in fact, once said, 'Christianity is forgiveness'. That is not the whole of it, but it is a most important part. Blue, then, stand for forgiveness. And here is my third and last story.

It is said that a Belgian priest was compelled to leave his village when the first War came and take refuge in France. He was an old man, and could do little in a practical way to help his country. But as soon as the war ended, he decided to return home. His friends did their best to dissuade him. They knew that he would be grieved beyond measure by the ruin of his old home. However, he was adamant. Much of the journey he made on foot, for most of his savings had gone. Eventually he reached the village where for so many years he had been the 'cure of souls'. He was horrified at what he saw. The devastation was indescribable, and the old man's heart sank within him.

Slowly he found his way among the ruins where once his beloved cottagers had lived and toiled, and made his way to the church. That, also, had not escaped. The roof had been blown off, three of the four walls were in ruins, and the whole place was in a state of chaos.

Seeing all the wreckage of a lifetime's labours, the old priest burst into tears. Presently, however, he noticed that one part of the church was almost intact, and that was the altar. With much difficulty the old man made his way up to the place where so often he had knelt in prayer and led his little flock in the Holy Sacrament. On his knees once more, he began to repeat those familiar words of the Lord's Prayer - only, of course, in the native tongue. 'Our Father, Which art in Heaven; Hallowed be Thy name; Thy kingdom come; Thy will be done on earth as it is in Heaven; give us this day our daily bread; and forgive us our trespasses as we.....' The voice faltered, and stopped. Thinking of the ruin around him, the priest could not forgive. A second time he started the prayer, and again broke down at the same place. A third attempt he made, but again broke down. But this time a most extraordinary thing happened. As the voice of the old man faltered and stopped, another voice took up the words, in clear and determined tones. 'Forgive us our trespasses, as we forgive them that trespass against us!' The priest rose to his feet. Who was the intruder? He looked, and amazement filled his eyes, for rumour has it that the intruder was none other than the King of the Belgians himself! The priest went towards the King, and bowed before him. Then the King led the priest to his own altar; there they knelt side by side and together, King and priest, repeated the Lord's Prayer from the beginning to end.

Forgiveness is not easy. Yet, unless we can live in the spirit of forgiveness, we can scarcely live at all! And you remember what Jesus said - the only comment He ever made on His own great prayer - 'If ye forgive not men their trespasses, neither will your Father forgive you.' Blue must stand for forgiveness.

Now what have we? Red for courage; white for purity; blue for forgiveness. Perhaps you will say, 'That's all very lovely and necessary, but Oh! so hard!' Of course it is. But there is one thing to help you. What is the background of our Union Jack? Is it not the red cross of St George? And does that not remind you of the background of our Christianity, the Cross of Jesus Christ? Here is the secret: so long as we live in the spirit of that Cross, so long as we let Jesus live in our hearts, we shall be courageous, and pure and forgiving. So I come, at last, to my text: 'I can do all things through Christ who strengtheneth me.'

I would be true, for there are those who
trust me;
I would be pure, for there are those who
care:
I would be brave, for there is much to
suffer;
I would be strong, for there is much to
dare.
I would be friend of all, the foe, the
friendless;
I would be giving, and forget the gift:
I would be humble, for I know my
weakness;
I would look up, and laugh, and love, and
lift.

And you can only do that 'through Christ'.

Britain

The next time you see the Union Jack flying in the breeze, will you remember, red for courage, white for purity, blue for forgiveness?

A PRAYER

Heavenly Father take away from us those things which hinder our approach to You. We depend upon You for life itself.

We hate the selfishness that characterises so much of our living and prevents us from fellowship with our fellows and from knowing You.

Teach us how to forgive and forget, and how to love our neighbours as ourselves.

Help us to be patient with those whose opinions differ from our own. Keep us faithful in our witness of our Christian Faith.

THE ELF AND THE SHOES

Once upon a time there were two houses side by side, and in these two houses there lived two families. The little boy who lived in one house was very friendly with the little girl who lived in the other house. The lady who lived in one house had many friendly chats with the lady who lived in the other. But the man who lived in one house was always quarrelling with the man who lived in the other. The cause of all of the trouble was the two gardens.

For you must know that the first man had a most beautiful garden, and was exceedingly proud of his flowers. The man in the other house grew very few flowers, but he had some poultry, and spent a great deal of time with his hens.

All went well until one day the hens found a little hole in the fence that divided the two gardens, and, scrambled thorough, they scratched up all the seeds and damaged many of the flowers of the beautiful garden. When the man who owned it saw what was happening he flew into a great rage, and shouted to the other man 'Come and look what your hens have done to my garden'.

Now as it happened the other man had got up in a very bad temper that morning. He was troubled with indigestion, and he felt very much out of sorts. So instead of telling his neighbour how sorry he was, he said crossly, 'Well, you should not have let them into your garden.'

64

This made the first man more angry than ever, and he stormed back, 'Let them in! Whoever heard of such a thing. As if I wanted your dirty old hens. They have got through a hole in the fence.'

The owner of the hens did not like them called 'dirty,' so he responded sharply, 'Well, you should keep your fence in better repair.'
'That is not my job, but yours,' replied the other angrily.

'Oh no, it is not,' said the first man. 'You are responsible for that fence, and also for the damage your hens have caused. Let me tell you that if I find any of your hens again in my garden, I will ring their necks.'

'And let me tell you,' said the owner of the hens, 'that if I find any of my hens missing, I shall have the law on you for stealing.'

So they went on storming and quarrelling, until at last, in a terrible rage, they went in and slammed the doors of their houses. When they were inside they started to vent their bad tempers on their families.

The man who owned the beautiful garden said, 'I never heard such impertinence in my life. Saying that I shall have to mend the fence. He must think that I am a fool.' And he then told his wife and little boy that they must never on any account have anything to do with the people next door.

The man to whom the hens belonged told his family the same thing. 'I never did like that man, and I never wish to speak to him again. From now onwards, you must neither of you speak to those folks. They are not worth speaking to.'

So because of the bad temper of the two men, two families were miserable. The ladies went about their work in silence, feeling very unhappy because they could no longer break off to have their little chats. And the boy and girl felt most miserable, for they had now to play alone, and they missed each other sorely.

The little girl probably felt it most of all, and after a very lonely day, she lay in bed crying herself to sleep. Then suddenly she heard a squeaky little voice which said, 'Come on, cheer up. It won't help things to cry, will it?'

She looked up and saw, seated at the bottom of the bed, was a tiny little elf. His long ears stood straight up at each side of his little green cap; his dark eyes gleamed like little beads; and his huge mouth extended from ear to ear in a comical grin. In spite of herself she had to smile.

'That's better,' said the elf. 'Now supposing you tell me all about it.'

The girl felt so comforted by the way in which the elf spoke that she lay down again, and in a short time was fast asleep. The elf turned head over heels off the bed, and then crept out of the room. He then crept along the passage till he came to the bedroom of the man of the house. Opening the door quietly, he crept in, and felt along the floor until he found the man's shoes. Picking these up, he crept out again, shutting the door quietly behind him.

Quickly passing out of the house into the garden, he climbed thorough the hole in the fence, and went into the house of the next door neighbour. Here again he crept upstairs until he reached the room of the man of the house, and, opening the door quietly, he placed the shoes he carried by the side of the bed. Then he picked up this other man's shoes, and hurried back to the first house. In a very short time he had placed the other pair of shoes by the side of the first man's bed. Then with a quiet chuckle, he ran off to his little home in the wood nearby.

The next morning the people in each of the houses were delighted to find that the men were in much better tempers. The man who owned the beautiful garden came down to his breakfast smiling, and said, 'I have been thinking about the quarrel I had with my neighbour last night. After all, he is not a bad sort of a fellow, and it was not his fault that his hens got through into my garden. I did not like to admit it yesterday, but it is my job to keep that fence in repair, and if I had done so, then the hens would not have got through. I think I will have to speak to him about it.'

And the man who owned the hens was saying a similar thing to the people in the house.

'I am sorry I lost my temper yesterday with that chap next door. After all, he had enough to make him angry. He had spent a lot of time growing those beautiful flowers and it was a pity that my hens did all that damage. I will go and tell him how sorry I am.'

So, in a very short time, they were chatting quite friendly over the fence. The man who owned the beautiful garden had promised to have the fence repaired, and the man who owned the hens had promised to pay for the damage that had been done. The first man sent a bunch of flowers to the lady of the other house, and his neighbour sent a basket of eggs to the other lady. And best of all, the boy and girl were soon playing quite happily together.

That night the little girl had hardly settled down in bed when she again heard the squeaky voice, and there was the elf at the foot of the bed, with the cheerful little grin on his face.

'I told you I would fix it, didn't I?' he said with a laugh.

'Why , yes,' replied the girl, clapping her hands, 'and you have succeeded wonderfully. You must be very clever. How did you do it?'

'Oh, it was easy. I just changed their shoes.'

'Changed their shoes!' repeated the girl. 'What good would that do?'

The little elf laughed again. 'All the good in the world. You see, they stood in each other's shoes, and when people do that, they see things very differently. Your father saw things from the standpoint of the man who owned the beautiful garden, and the man who owned the beautiful garden saw things from the standpoint of your father. So it was easy for them to make it up.'

And because of the clever little elf who changed the shoes, they all lived happily ever after.

Don't you think it is something like this that is meant by the writer of the Epistle to the Hebrews when he said, 'Let us consider one another, to provoke unto love and good works'?

BENJAMIN

HYMN AS PRAYER

O Master let me walk with Thee
In lowly paths of service free;
Tell me Thy secret; help me bear
The strain of toil, the fret of care.

Help me the slow of heart to move
By some clear winning word of love;
Teach me the wayward feet to stay,
And guide them in the homeward way.

Teach me Thy patience; still with Thee
In closer, dearer company,
In work that keeps faith sweet and strong,
In trust that triumphs over wrong.

In hope that sends a shining ray
Far down the future's broadening way,
In peace that only Thou canst give,
With Thee, O Master, let me live. Amen.

KING'S JESTER

Once upon a time there was a little 'funny man'. His name was Rahere - R.A.H.E.R.E. He was the king's jester. He wore a little red suit and little red shoes with pointed toes, and a little pointed cap with bells and he knew a great many tricks.

Noble men and princes and kings in their castles liked to have a little jester around to help pass the time and to keep the fun merry. They were rough old days, but Rahere enjoyed his life well enough in the Court of King Henry the First.

Then suddenly, one day, everything in the Court was changed. Even the gay heart of little Rahere was changed. The loss of the famous White Ship and the drowning of the Crown Prince brought sadness to King and courtiers alike.

In a very short time, little Rahere was off to Rome on a pilgrimage. It was usual for very good people to do that in those days. Their pilgrimages sometimes took them a very long time and were full of dangers. Little Rahere, whose heart had been full of fun, was not one to shirk a dangerous task, and at last he arrived in Rome.

But after he had been there a little while, he fell sick in that distant city. So sick was he that he thought he was going to die. Afraid, he did what many people do when they are sick and afraid - he prayed, and he made a promise to God.

He promised that if God would only let him get better and go home again, he would do something for the sick people of his own land.

And at last, God heard his prayer, and little Rahere, by degrees, got better.

Lots of people forget their promises once they are better. But Rahere didn't He said, 'A promise is a promise'. And he was the more eager about it when one night he had a dream in which it seemed to him that a man of great strength and straightness and beauty stood before him.

'Pray, who are you?' asked Rahere, looking up. 'Pray, tell me who you are?'

'I am Bartholomew, the Apostle of Jesus', said the man of great strength and straightness and beauty. 'I have come to help you. For your great purpose, choose a place in London at the Smooth-field. Only ask for it, and you shall receive it; seek for it and you shall find it. Have no fears about how the work shall be done. It is my work to help you'.

When Rahere awakened he was more than ever eager to get on with his promise. So he put on his clothes of a friar - a plain brown coat tied with a rope at the waist - and after a long time he stood again at the ante-room of the King's chamber.

At first his old court friends did not know him. Rahere the little funny man turned serious! At first they thought it the best joke of all.

But it wasn't a joke. Now that he was fit and strong, Rahere hadn't forgotten his promise.

'I have business whereof I would speak with the King', said Rahere. And when the King bade him draw near, he asked him for that piece of ground about which he had heard in his dream.

'The Smooth-field!' said those who stood listening. 'The little man must be mad! That flat, wet, marshy place is fit only for the horses that run there, and for the hangman's gallows that stands there. It's a terrible place!'

But little Rahere went next morning to the Smooth-field, wet, and waste; and the people passing by laughed at him.

But the children who came to play on the Smooth-field liked the little man in the plain brown coat tied with a rope at the waist. He played games with them, and then he asked them for their help to gather the smooth stones that lay about. Soon the children began to tell their fathers and mothers at home what was happening at the Smooth-field and they, too, came to help. Rahere explained his plan to all who came and soon half the people of London, it seemed, had heard what was happening. Courtiers came to jeer, but they were so struck by the honesty of the work, and the joy of those who served in it, that they felt that they had to leave gifts of gold behind. Horse dealers came, who held a market on the Smooth-field, and they too gave help as they could.

So the building rose higher and higher until at last the Smooth-field was changed altogether, and where there had been waste and wet and rubbish there rose a Church, a Priory and a Hospital - named after St Bartholomew, whom Rahere had seen in his dream.

Rahere's hospital was a plain, clean place, but to the poor, sick people it seemed like Heaven. Not only did they feel the kindness and tenderness of it, but they felt that it all belonged to God. Soon they needed more room for those who came, and Rahere had to get more stones and bricks and make it bigger.

Rahere made his promise and built his hospital a long time ago now - for he died in 1140 but his work still goes on. Today, there stands on part of the Smooth-fields, now called Smithfield, a great hospital, St Bart's - short for St Bartholomew's - the most famous hospital in all London. And nearby is the little church, part of which Rahere built himself.

And that is the story of the little 'funny man'.

Can you keep your promises? Little Rahere could. He promised to do something for the sick people and he never forgot. He said 'A promise is a promise!'

HYMN AS PRAYER

Take my life, and let it be
Consecrated, Lord, to Thee;
Take my moments and my days,
Let them flow in ceaseless praise.

Take my hands, and let them move
At the impulse of Thy love;
Take my feet, and let them be
Swift and beautiful for Thee.

Take my voice, and let me sing
Always, only, for my King;
Take my lips, and let them be
Filled with messages from Thee.

Take my silver and my gold,
Not a mite would I withhold;
Take my intellect, and use
Every power as Thou shalt choose.

Take my will, and make it Thine;
It shall be no longer mine;
Take my heart, it is Thine own;
It shall be Thy royal throne.

Take my love, my Lord, I pour
At Thy feet its treasure-store;
Take myself, and I will be
Ever, only, all for Thee.
                              Amen.

PLAYING SECOND FIDDLE

If you go into Devonshire, you meet Sir Francis Drake. You cannot help it. In Plymouth, roads and terraces and an island in the Sound are called after him, a reservoir, even a kind of local sweet: and there upon the Hoe is his famous statue which is a copy of the original one at Tavistock where he was born in 1540.

Now if you ask most people about Drake they will know that he was a sea-dog and he played bowls and he had something to do with the Spanish Armada. But they won't know very much more. As a matter of fact there are lots of things that we don't know about Francis Drake's life. For instance we can go and see the wonderful old church where he was married to Mary on July 4, 1569. But we only know one single other thing about his wife, and that is the date of her death! We know that two years before he was married Drake sailed on his first voyage westwards. He sailed with Captain John Lovell, and; the only thing we know that he did on the voyage is something found in some old Mexican records. It says that during the voyage he won Michael Morgan to know and love Jesus Christ. This came out when Morgan was tried by the Mexican Inquisition for being a Protestant. He had been converted by Drake. So the bold seaman was a bold and believing Christian too.

A second interesting thing we find out about Drake is this. When, at the age of 34, he set sail round the world, he took with him his young cousin, John Drake. The days must sometimes have seemed long on board the slow sailing-ship, but happily these two shared a hobby together. They both loved drawing and painting charts. I suspect that the supple fingers of the lad did a neater job than the hands of the hardy sea-man and fighter, but Drake had wonderful patience. That comes out in something that a man who wrote his life-story said of him, that he was always learning - deliberately - and most of all from his own mistakes. It isn't the man who makes no mistakes who is great and wise, but the man who is humble and teachable enough to learn from them.

But the true greatness of Drake comes out with the coming of the Spanish Armada in 1588. No: it wasn't at that game of bowls, although that was a bit of sauciness that pleases us all. It was this. Drake had expected, and indeed everyone else had expected too, that he would be appointed to command the English Navy against the Armada. He had fought in the West Indies: he had singed the King of Spain's beard: he had sailed round the world. He was the most famous seaman alive. He was not, however, appointed to command the Navy of England. The Queen and her councillors thought it wiser to appoint Lord Howard to command, with Drake as second-in-command. How did Drake take that? We are told, 'He played second fiddle with an admirable cheerfulness.' 'Sir,' wrote Lord Howard later to one of the Queen's Secretaries, 'I must not omit to let you know how lovingly and kindly Sir Francis Drake beareth himself; and also how dutifully to her Majesty's service and unto me, being in the place I am in.' That is something worth knowing and remembering about Drake.

A big man takes second place cheerfully. He is there only to do his duty. Whether he is captain of the team or vice-captain of just one of the players does not matter. What matters is that duty be done and each man's part be played. Remember that as we see it happen in the life of one of England's heroes, a man who could play second fiddle cheerfully.

HYMN AS PRAYER

Just as I am, Thine own to be,
Friend of the young who lovest me,
To consecrate myself to Thee,
      O Jesus Christ, I come.

In the glad morning of my day,
My life to give, my vows to pay,
With no reserve and no delay,
      With all my heart I come.

I would live ever in the light,
I would work ever for the right,
I would serve Thee with all my might,
      Therefore to Thee I come.

Just as I am, young, strong, and free,
To be the best that I can be
For truth and righteousness and Thee,
      Lord of my life, I come.

DRAGON'S BONES

You get some queer kinds of medicine even now, don't you? It can have a queer look, a queer smell, a queer taste, to say nothing of what it does. But you trust the doctor, the chemist, the nurse: you swallow it down and it does you good.

Of course, in the old days they put some very queer things into medicines. In fact, they seem to have imagined that the more weird the ingredients were, the more wonderful the medicine would be, so in went toads and spiders and pearls and hairs. Now in old China they greatly fancied dragons' bones. Ground up and put into medicine they would cure anything: but, when all is said and done, there were a lot of sick people in China and not so many dragons. So, one day, a farmer in An-Yang in the province North Hunan was very excited when his plough turned up some bones onto the surface of the land. They were queerish looking, not very big, indeed they were all much of a muchness for size, but obviously very old, obviously dragons' bones. He went to the chemist, who made up the medicines, and offered his dragons' bones for sale. They bought them up eagerly. The patients took the medicine eagerly. The farmer became rich. So did the chemists. What happened to the patients, I don't know. We can only hope that the bones did them no harm.

When the bones came out of the ground, they were dirty. It was the chemists job to wash them. When they did so, they noticed some black marks on them, squiggles rather like writing, but they couldn't make anything of the marks, so they just scraped them off and had nice, clean dragons' bones. This supply of bones became famous, and some of China's scholars became curious as to where they could all have come from. They went to see the place where the bones were being dug up by the thousand. They examined them before they were washed, before they were scraped. They noticed the black squiggles and found that it was the earliest written Chinese, dated between 1765 and 1123 B.C. People were writing on those bones when Joseph was in Egypt, when our Stonehenge was being built.

That is not all the story. The land was carefully excavated, and what scholars guessed was then proved to be true. There had once been a great Temple on this spot, say between three and four thousand years ago. The old people of the land had come to it to pray, to ask God's help. Because they were simple and ignorant there was much that they wanted to know from God. They wrote down on a piece of fresh bone in ink what it was that they wanted to ask the gods. The priest then put the bone into a kind of oven. That dried and roasted it and made it crack. Then, the priest used to pretend to read the cracks as a sort of secret writing, the answer of the gods. Having got their answer, I suppose the people just threw the bones away and that is why those fields were so full of them.

So, when we see one of these bones in a museum, and that is where they go now and not into medicine, we are looking at a prayer, a queer prayer and a queer answer. We are not to laugh or jeer at those folk. They knew no better. They needed God just as we do. They wanted to talk to Him and they wanted an answer. Think how very blest we are who know how simply we may speak to God and how lovingly He answers. What a lot of trouble they went to, perhaps making a long journey to the Temple, finding the right bone, getting someone to write on it, probably having to make a costly offering, having the bone baked and then getting someone to read the answer. We do not have to go through all that performance to make our requests known to God. It is easier for us. We must take care that that does not make us grow careless about our prayers.

A PRAYER

O God our Heavenly Father we know that life is very wonderful and very precious. We also believe that everyone of us has a divinely appointed mission to fulfil.

If Your plan for us has been spoiled because of our waywardness, forgive us and lead us again into the appointed way that we may become a blessing to all with whom we have to do, and that our joy may be real in the knowledge that we do Your will.

THEOPHILUS VISITS THE QUEEN

His surname was a very common one. It was Smith. Perhaps that is why his parents gave him such an uncommon Christian name. They called him Theophilus. It comes out of the Bible and it means 'friend of God', which is just what he grew up to be.

This Theophilus Smith was a farmer living at Attleborough in Norfolk, well over a hundred years ago. He was deeply interested in his work and he invented an improved plough. Because of that he was commanded to go to Windsor Castle to be received by Queen Victoria - a very great honour indeed.

So Theophilus travelled to Windsor the day before his audience with the Queen. He went straight to the lodge at the Castle gate. The porter in the lodge suggested that he should stay the night at one of the inns in the town and then come to the Castle in good time in the morning. At this the simple farmer grew quite cross.

The colonel of the guard, who was standing by and saw what was happening, tried to pacify Theophilus, but he exclaimed, 'Look here, if you came to Attleborough to see me, my wife would have a bed ready for you, especially if we had asked you to come. And if you were hungry as I am, I warrant she would find you something good to eat.' The colonel was so sorry to see Theophilus so put out that he took him to his own quarters for the night and gave him some supper and a bed.

The next morning Theophilus went back to the Castle. First he saw the Queen's husband, Prince Albert, who gave permission for the plough to be named after himself. Then came the audience with the Queen. 'Queen' is such a splendid word that most people forget that a Queen is just
a woman, a wife, a mother. After his audience our farmer said that he was surprised to find Queen Victoria was 'a comely, simple woman with a kind look'.

They talked about the plough, but that was not enough for Theophilus Smith, the friend of God, the man who loved the little Baptist Church at Attleborough and all its ways. He wanted to speak to the Queen about his friend. Suddenly he saw his opportunity.

'However,' asked the Queen, 'did you come to think of this clever idea? Was it very hard, and did it take you a long time to work it out?'

'Well, Ma'am,' replied Theophilus, 'I had the idea in my head for some time fore I could get it straight. So I made it a matter of prayer: and one morning I saw it all in a flash.'

'What,' said the Queen, 'you prayed about this plough?'

'Yes, Ma'am,' said Theophilus, 'I prayed about my plough because I pray about everything. Why not?' And then he went on, 'May I tell your Majesty something?'

The Queen nodded, and he told her this story.

'When one of my boys was only a little chap I bought him a whip. He was pleased as could be. He went round pretending to drive his horses and cracking his whip in fine style. Then one day he came to me crying fit to break his little heart. He had given something an extra smart blow with the whip and it was broken. He held the pieces out to me. Now, Ma'am, the whip was nothing to me. It only cost a copper of two. But it was everything to the boy. When I saw his tears over it, I stopped what I was doing and sat down and took him on my knee and comforted him. I couldn't bear to see him so troubled, and I put the whip right again. Don't you think that our Heavenly Father cares as much for me as I care for my boy? My plough may not be very important to God, but I believed that because it mattered to me He would help me with it if I asked Him. That is why I prayed about my plough.'

So we see the good farmer ready and glad to say a word for God to a Queen. We see a man whose daily work was done with prayer. And we see a man who knew that our Heavenly Father cares about the smallest thing that matters to us. Of all the sowing that ever he did, nothing was finer than this, to plant a seed of faith in prayer in the heart of a Queen, of a child.

A PRAYER

Dear Lord, we do not, and never can deserve the least of Your mercies, but we are glad that no blessing is denied us in spite of our waywardness. Help us to be grateful and to live as grateful people.

May everything we do and say reflect not us but Your glory. Grant that people seeing us may want to know You.

Speed the day Lord when everyone in every land will acknowledge that You are the only True God and Jesus Christ whom you have sent to us.

DR GRENFELL AND POOR POMIUK

Grenfell was at Navchak when he first heard of poor Pomiuk. There are three names thrown straight at you. What do they mean?

Wilfred Grenfell was the great missionary doctor who began caring for the tough brave people of Labrador. There were over 3,000 English, Irish and Scottish, a few Indians, and about 1,700 Eskimos. They all got their living by fishing for cod.

In 1895, when the ice and fog of the long, harsh winter began to clear, Dr. Grenfell made his way along the coast from settlement to settlement. He came at last to Navchak, where the great mountains come down to the sea in sheer cliffs, and where the Hudson's Bay Company had a trading post.

There, at Navchak, Dr. Grenfell first heard of Pomiuk. Pomiuk was an Eskimo boy whose father had been murdered when he was small. His mother married again and went away, leaving little Pomiuk with a man called Kupah. Five years before Grenfell came to Navchak, a man had arrived who was looking for a few real Eskimos who would go back with him to Chicago and be shown in the famous World Fair. Kupah was one who listened and, taking little Pomiuk with him, he set out for Chicago. There the Eskimos appeared every day in what was called 'Eskimo Village'. One of the things they did was to show the visitors to the Fair their skill with the long whips used in driving the dog-teams which pulled their sledges. The visitors would throw coins, and as they fell Kupah and Pomiuk would flash out the long whip and flick the coin towards themselves.

While he was at the Fair Pomiuk had an accident. He broke his thigh. Then all that he could do was sit about and watch the others. He would have been very lonely but for an American Congregational minister called George Carpenter, who was only in Chicago for ten days, but who went to see Pomiuk and cheer him up every one of those days. When he left Chicago he promised to write a letter and send his photograph to the boy.

When the World Fair was over, the Eskimos were taken back as far as Newfoundland and left to make their own way home to North Labrador, 2,000 miles away. And, remember, Pomiuk was handicapped and ill. This is where Wilfred Grenfell comes in. When he arrived at Navchak he was told that there was a letter for Pomiuk and was asked if he would try and find the boy and read it to him. It was a letter from the Rev. George Carpenter. Someone had heard of a boy lying ill in a tent, further inland. Believing this might be Pomiuk, Grenfell set out to search for him and found him lying dirty, neglected and in pain. His broken thigh had never properly healed and poison from the wound was gradually spreading.

Dr. Wilfred Grenfell got Kupah's permission to take Pomiuk aboard his launch, where he dressed the horrible, painful wounds and then took him southwards. On the journey the wounds had to be dressed every day.

It hurt terribly, and in order to encourage the boy to be brave Grenfell used to mark up in chalk on a cupboard door 'G' for 'Good' when he didn't cry, and 'B' for 'Bad' when he did. But more than this, Grenfell told Pomiuk about Jesus Christ. They stopped at one of the settlements called Hopedale and there Pomiuk was baptised and given the names Gabriel Pomiuk. He was taught to sing some simple hymns, and even learned to play the concertina. He also learned to draw and write. By the time they got back to Grenfell's base, the boy was clean, happy and full of love for his kind new friend.

One of the first things they did then was to send a message to the Rev. George Carpenter to tell him that Pomiuk had been found and that he was being looked after and would probably stay with Grenfell for a whole year, until he was really well. Mr Carpenter wrote back at once, 'How much will it cost to keep Pomiuk for a year?' When he heard how much was needed, he asked the boys and girls of America to give it. 'He belongs to us; let us take care of him'. And this not only helped Pomiuk, it helped Dr. Grenfell. People heard about his work, and they wanted to know more and to help by giving money to that.

What happened to Pomiuk? All was not well with that leg. It had been neglected for too long. It refused to heal. So he was moved to another, bigger hospital. He was there for Christmas, and this is the letter he wrote to tell his friends what a marvellous time he had:

Me got a nice time at Xmas, sweets and a cake.

Lot of little girls and boys got a tea. It makes
them laugh to look at Xmas big tree. Sister got
Tommy
and me jack in box. I opened box. I very
frightened
and make people laugh very much. I make paper
chains very long for sister, also candles in
lanterns,
very pretty ... I want a letter by and bye, please.
Me   like to see you next year. I'm sorry you
stop home ... Aukshenai (Goodbye), Dr. Grenfell, very
much, Gabriel Pomiuk.

I suppose that in some ways that was Pomiuk's
first Christmas. It was the first time he had been with
Christian people who knew what it meant and who kept
Christmas with the old ways. It was also his last. For, in
a little while he grew worse and died.

But, wherever the story of Pomiuk was told,
people knew that the Christian missionary doctor could
bring to people like him both medicines and a message.
The medicines were to comfort and help in illness and
pain. The message told of One who loved them, sick or
well, living or dying. Such doctors and nurses need the
support of our gifts to make the work possible. They
need the support of our prayers, and so do those they
seek to serve.

A PRAYER

Lord Jesus. The disciples once asked to be taught how to Pray.

Teach me Lord how to pray - teach me how to shut out all the noises of life and know how to be still in Your Presence, how to be quiet - how to listen.

Teach me to be sensitive as I listen for the answers to my prayers through my conscience - my reading and my friends and all the other ways in which You try to speak to me. Help me to sit still, be quiet and Listen.

THE BOOK OF THE FREE

A thousand years ago there were very, very few books in England. Those that were had all been written by hand: for they were the days before printing.

These hand-written books were beautifully done, often by monks in the quiet of their monasteries. If you see them, you can hardly believe that they were hand-written, the lines are so regular. Each letter is carefully made. The capital letters stand up, large and clear. And when the book is the Bible, the first letter of a chapter may be big and beautiful, coloured with glowing red or blue or gold, and sometimes a little picture is drawn round the shape of the large letter.

Such a book is the Bodmin Gospels. It was written just about 1,000 years ago, and it is the only book, notice that, the only book of all those in the monasteries of Cornwall which has survived to our day. It gives, in Latin, the Gospel portions to be read as Lessons at the great church services, and it has those beautiful capital letters, 'illuminated' as we call them, 'made to shine' as that long word means. This book of the Bodmin Gospels was probably written out in France and then it came to belong to the Cornish monastery of St. Petoc in Padstow.

I said books were scarce. Paper was almost unknown. So, every bit of writing space was used. On the clean end pages of this book, at the top and bottom and in the margins of the pages, there is writing, notes of special business done at the monastery long ago. What was the business? The setting free of slaves. What sort of slaves? Coloured slaves, like those that Wilberforce and Clarkson worried about? No. We are thinking of days long before that, when there were slaves here in England. They belonged to their masters, with all their family, and they dared not to leave his place. But when this old book was being used in the daily services of the monastery of St. Petroc, the richer folk in that part of Cornwall were just beginning to see that it was wrong to hold their fellow-countrymen as slaves. So they began to set them free. This was solemnly done in public before the great altar, and a record of it somewhere written into this book.

You stand and look at the old writing and you suddenly realise that this was about men. This marked a wonderful day in their lives, the day when they were set free for ever.

Actually there are 47 separate entries, covering 122 slaves, between the years A.D. 940 - 1040. Of these slaves, 98 were Cornish, 12 were Saxon and the other 12 were of various nationalities. These 122 slaves belonged to 33 masters. And when the monks wrote down that their masters were setting these slaves free, they wrote 38 times in Latin and 9 times in English, and they signed their names as witnesses of what had been done. Let me just give you a sample of the sort of thing they wrote, in Latin and in English:

Hoc est nomen illius hominis quem liberavit XYZ ....

Thes ys taes nama dhe XYZ gefreade ...

'This is the name of the man whom XYZ (that is just my name for the master) has set free ...'

Why did they write it in this book? First, because the book was in the care of the monastery and therefore likely to last. The record would be preserved. If there was any dispute later about whether the man was free or not, he could always appeal to what was written here. Second, because it was thought that to set a slave free was a good thing to do, and simple men wrote it in one of God's books to make sure that God knew all about it! He would then do good to those who had done good. Third, because in this very book Jesus said to His disciples, 'No longer do I call you servants (and the word is really 'Slaves') ... But I have called you friends'. He sets all His followers free to be not His slaves but His friends. So, later, His followers came to see that they must set each other free. 'There can be neither bond (slave) nor free ... Ye are all one in Christ Jesus'. Because they were all His friends, they were friends to one another. That was why it felt right and good that those who gave freedom to a slave should record it in this book through which Christ gives life and liberty to all men.

This book quite rightly became the Book of the Free. I like to think that my name is there, and yours, because we too are His friends.

A PRAYER

Heavenly Father, because I am so conscious of my own needs and wants I often forget the needs of other people - forgive me and make me sensitive to other people.

Help us to remember that the unknown circumstances of other people may be the reason for their actions and attitudes.

Give me patience and understanding and the ability to hear and understand their point of view; that we may both grow in Goodness and Grace.

THE GLASS THAT DID NOT BREAK

Here is something to reckon out. If Mary Honywood died in 1620 aged 93, in what year was she born? The right answer is 1527. That is fairly easy. But is your history as good as your arithmetic? Who was King of England then? Henry VIII. So this woman was born under Henry VIII, lived through the reigns of Edward VI, Mary, Elizabeth ! and James !. She lived during the reigns of three kings and two queens, and at the same time as Drake, Sir Walter Raleigh, Shakespeare.

They were exciting times in our history, and of all the great changes that were happening perhaps the greatest was the change that came to the Church of England. Mary Honywood was born into a Church that was Roman Catholic and she died in one that was Protestant and now called itself 'The Church of England', whose leader was not the Pope in Rome but the Archbishop in Canterbury. While this change was coming, kings and queens were cruel to those who would not take their point of view, and laws and punishments were severe. Mary became a Protestant under Henry and Edward. When Catholic Queen Mary put Protestants in prison, at a great risk, Mary Honywood stuck to her own opinions and went and visited the prisoners. When John Bradford was burned to death at Smithfield for being a Protestant, Mary went to see this dreadful sight, perhaps with the idea of giving some comfort to the poor man, What suddenly makes the whole horrible thing real to us is that we are told that the crowd was tremendous., and in the pushing about Mary lost a shoe and had to limp home with only one.

When she died at Charing in Essex, Mary Honywood was 93, and she left 367 descendants. Perhaps you had better add up to see if that is right. She had 16 children, 114 grandchildren, 228 great-grandchildren, and 9 great-great-granchildren. It means that she could have had a birthday to remember every day of the year, with 2 to spare! Once, before she died, her relatives said they would give her a banquet and 200 gathered. We are told there would have been more but the roads were bad. It must have been marvellous to move in and out among all these people and to feel that they all belonged to her. They were all her folk and family.

Yet, this strong, tough woman, living so long and so many to take care of her, was worried. She worried about whether she herself really belonged to God's family, whether He could possibly love her and take her to live for ever with Him after her death. Would she be 'saved' or would she be 'lost'? This was what deeply worried her. All the sermons she heard and all the prayers she said seemed to bring her little comfort.

One day, the famous writer John Foxe went to see her. He was the man who wrote a great book about how martyrs like John Bradford died in the dreadful days of Queen Mary. He found Mary Honywood very depressed and anxious. She talked to him of how undeserving she was of God's love, of how wicked she was at heart. Suddenly she took up a glass from the table and dashed it to the ground, saying 'I am as certain to be lost as this glass is to break'.

She and John Foxe alike must have looked at it open-eyed, wondering and almost afraid, for it did not break!

Then, I believe, she took comfort and realised that she was not certain to be lost. For there is no limit to the love of God, no end. Just as the father of the Prodigal Son went on loving him, however far off he went, and longed for his return, and ran out of the gate to meet him when he came back from the far country, so God loves, on and on. He showed us that in Jesus - that He will forgive all that is wrong and will love us to the end, and beyond - for ever and ever. Jesus said that He came to seek the lost and to save them, to bring them back home to God's love and care. There is no need to be anxious. We can quietly trust His love and power who said, 'The man who comes to me I will never turn away'.

HYMN PRAYER

God be in my head,
  And in my understanding;
God be in mine eyes,
  And in my looking;
God be in my mouth,
  And in my speaking;
God be in my heart,
  And in my thinking;
God be at mine end,
  And at my departing.
        Amen.

A PRAYER

Heavenly Father we give thanks today for the coming into our world of our Saviour, Jesus Christ and for His teaching and His example and for the tremendous price He paid in dying for us on the Cross.

Help us to be faithful witnesses of Him, and to reflect only His Glory, and not the doubts and fears that so often plague us. Grant that people may want to know Him because of what they see of Him in us.

Through Jesus Christ our Lord.

Amen.

THE TEACHER WITH INFLUENZA

Once there was a lovely teacher call Alice Freeman Palmer. She lived in America, and she was the head of a great college.

But what was really the best thing about her was that she had influenza for years and years.

You mustn't think that odd, or start to feel sorry for the teacher, or for the pupils in that great college. It wasn't that kind of influenza - it was a god kind of influenza, not the bad kind that you get in the winter when you've kept your wet shoes on, or played alongside somebody with the sniffles and sneezes. Then, of course, you have to stay indoors, and have lots of handkies and nasty sticky throat lozenges. And if you have it really badly, you have to stay in bed, and have the doctor come to take your temperature and look at your tongue. And when he has gone, you have to shake up the big bottle of medicine he has prescribed, and take it until it's all gone. And there's no getting out of it - because you have influenza, a very nasty thing.

Do you know how that nasty thing got its name? Well, when it first came to England, nobody knew much about it. Except that it was a sickness that one person got from another - it was catching. If a boy or a girl sitting alongside another in a desk at school started sniffing and sneezing, it wasn't very long before the other was sniffing and sneezing too.

And the doctors looked for a long-sounding name to give that sickness. And they decided on an Italian name - Influenza - which really means something that flows out of one life into the lives of others round about.

And it was really a very good name, wasn't it, although the sickness that it stands for is an altogether nasty kind of influenza.

But you see, you can have a good kind, too. That's why I said that that lovely teacher, Alice Freeman Palmer, teacher of that great college, had 'influenza' all her life. She did - she had influence, to use our English word for the good kind of influenza. She had a happy face and a happy heart, and she was wise and kind, and the girls loved her.

A long time after she was grown up, one girl wrote: 'When I saw her, I felt as if I could do things that I never dreamed of before. Even now, whenever I think of her, I have a sense of dignity in my life.' (Dignity is a nice true, good feeling.) 'I don't know what it is', she said. 'It seems as if her appreciation of the worth of things puts a spirit into me that carries me along until the next time I think of her. I shouldn't care to go on living in a world where she hadn't been.' Wasn't that a lovely thing to say?

She said she didn't know what it was - but we know what it was, don't we? It was influenza, or influence - the good kind - flowing happily out of the life of Alice Freeman Palmer, making others happy and true and glad, too.

For that's one thing about influenza, or influence - the good kind - that it's not easy to have it without others catching it. That's what Paul meant when he wrote in one of his letters that are collected in the back of our New Testaments: 'None of us liveth to himself' (Roman 14 7). And that's a happy thought; when we smile, other people are likely to catch it from us; when we stop to lend a hand, they are likely to catch the spirit of helpfulness; when we are brave, they are likely to be brave too. Once we're smiling, helpful and brave, we can't help them catching it from us - its just like influenza that puts us into bed, only much, much nicer. It's the good kind - influence. and every one of us has it, even the smallest, whether we think about it or not.

A PRAYER

Dear Lord and Master of us all we bless You for giving us all the good things in this life which we enjoy, especially our friends without whom life would be meaningless. We are thankful most of all for the friendship of Jesus, for the strength He gives us especially in times of stress and doubt and personal tragedy.

Help us so to live our lives that we shall enrich the World with our presence and make it a better place for everyone to live in just because we live in it.